Rex an
Creepy C........

Written by Rozanne Lanczak Williams
Created by Sue Lewis
Illustrated by Patty Briles

Creative Teaching Press

Rex and Tex's Creepy Creatures
© 2002 Creative Teaching Press, Inc.
Written by Rozanne Lanczak Williams
Illustrated by Patty Briles
Project Manager: Sue Lewis
Project Director: Carolea Williams

Published in the United States of America by:
Creative Teaching Press, Inc.
P.O. Box 2723
Huntington Beach, CA 92647-0723

All rights reserved. No part of this book may be reproduced in any form without the written permission of Creative Teaching Press, Inc.

CTP 3241

My creepy creature
has big teeth.

My creepy creature
has big feet.

My creepy creature
lives in a tree.

My creepy creature
reads books with me.

My creepy creature
eats weeds and beans.

Mine eats green ice cream.

My creepy creature is mean
and screams "E-e-e-e-e!"

And my creepy creature
is as sweet as can be!

Create your own book!

Use construction paper and collage materials to create your own creepy creature. Write and illustrate a book about your creature.

Words in *Rex and Tex's Creepy Creatures*

Long e		**High-Frequency Words**	**Other**
creepy	creature	and	lives
teeth	eats	my	books
feet	beans	has	mine
feed	cream	big	ice
weeds	mean	in	Rex
green	screams	a	Tex's
sweet	E-e-e-e-e	with	
tree		is	
be		as	
me		can	
reads			